Zaner-Bloser
Handwriting

swim

ZB Zaner-Bloser

Credits

Art: Mircea Catusanu/Painted Words: 3 (parrot), 14, 16, 18, 20, 22, 24, 26, 28, 30, 32, 35, 37; Nathan Jarvis: 3 (cat), 4, 84, 86, 92; Jan Bryan-Hunt/Painted Words: 6, 7, 102, 103, 111 (right), 112, 113; Tim Beaumont/Painted Words: 38, 40, 42, 44, 50, 52, 54, 56, 58, 60, 63; Cheryl Mendenhall/Cornell & McCarthy: 47; Gary Krejca/Wilkinson Studios: 66, 80, 81, 94, 95, 98; Bob Masheris/Wilkinson Studios: 68, 70, 72, 74, 75, 82, 83, 88, 91, 96; John Hovell: 110, 111 (spot art)

Literature: "City" by Langston Hughes, from *The Collected Poems of Langston Hughes,* by Langston Hughes. © 1994 by The Estate of Langston Hughes, Alfred A. Knopf, a division of Random House, Inc. Published by Random House, Inc. All rights reserved.

Photos: ©Paul Souders/Corbis: Cover; George C. Anderson Photography, Inc.: 5, 8, 9, 21; ©Blend Images/SuperStock: 49; ©Timothy Hearsum /Getty Images: 65; ©Janine Wiedel Photolibrary/Alamy: 77; ©Brand X Pictures/Jupiterimages: 116–117; ©Cordaiy Photo Library Ltd./CORBIS: 111; ©CEF/Getty Images: 96; ©NASA: 103

CONTENTS

Unit 4 Using What You Have Learned

Your Book

Models and Guidelines

There are writing models in your book. The models are on guidelines. The red arrows and numerals show you how to write each letter.

A ← Headline
← Midline
← Baseline
← Descender Space

Start at the green dot when you trace and write.

a

Handwriting Tutor

Scan the **Handwriting Tutor** codes with a mobile device to watch handwriting videos.

Stop and Check

 When you see a **Stop and Check** sign, circle the best letter you wrote on that line.

Circle the best letter on this line.

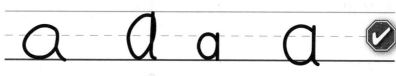

Handwriting Tutor

Keys to Legibility

Slant

Spacing

Size

Shape

There are four kinds of keys in your book. The words on the keys are **Shape, Size, Spacing,** and **Slant**.

Good writers think about these things when they write. The Keys will help you make your writing legible. **Legible** means easy to read.

Handwriting Tutor

Show What You Can Do

City
In the morning the city
Spreads its wings
Making a song
In stone that sings.

Write the title and the first four lines of the poem. Remember to leave space for margins.

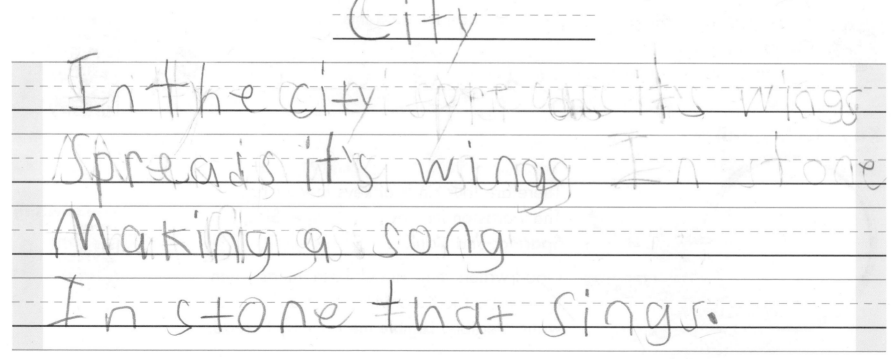

City

In the city spreads its wings
Spreads it's wings In stone
Making a song
In stone that sings.

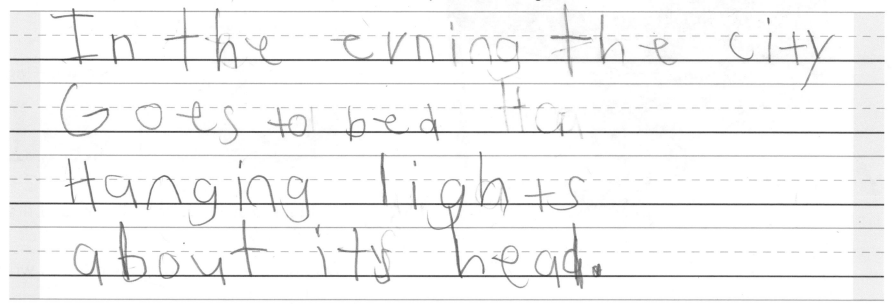

In the evening the city
Goes to bed
Hanging lights
About its head.

by Langston Hughes

Write the next four lines here. Remember to leave space for margins.

In the evning the city
Goes to bed Ha
Hanging lights
about its head.

If you write with your LEFT hand . . .

Sit like this.

Sit comfortably. Lean forward a little. Keep your feet flat on the floor.

Handwriting Tutor

Place the paper like this.

Handwriting Tutor

Slant the paper as shown in the picture.

Rest both arms on the desk. Use your right hand to move the paper as you write.

Pull the pencil toward your left elbow when you write.

Hold the pencil like this.

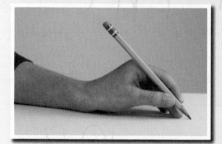

Handwriting Tutor

Hold the pencil with your thumb and first two fingers.

Do not squeeze the pencil when you write.

If you write with your **RIGHT** hand . . .

Sit like this.

Sit comfortably. Lean forward a little. Keep your feet flat on the floor.

Handwriting Tutor

Place the paper like this.

Handwriting Tutor

Place the paper straight in front of you.

Rest both arms on the desk. Use your left hand to move the paper as you write.

Pull the pencil toward the middle of your body when you write.

Hold the pencil like this.

Handwriting Tutor

Hold the pencil with your thumb and first two fingers.

Do not squeeze the pencil when you write.

Vertical Lines

Some letters and numerals have lines that are straight up and down.
Trace the straight up and down lines in these letters and numerals.

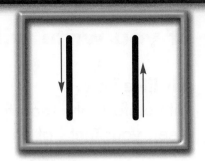

l b i p h T E L 5 4

Trace and write these letters and numerals that have vertical lines.
Start at the green dot.

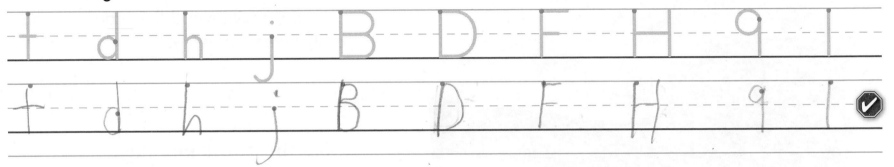

Write the sentence.

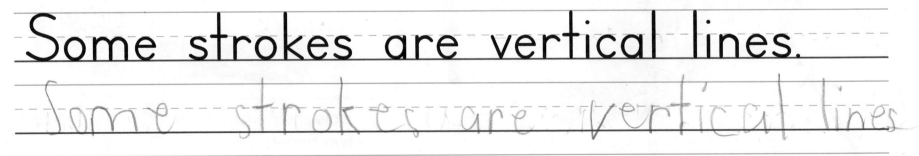

Some strokes are vertical lines.

10

Horizontal Lines

Some letters and numerals have lines that slide right or slide left.
Trace the slide lines in each letter and numeral.

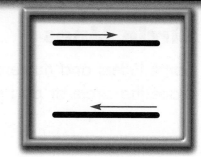

f f t e H J G Z 5 2

Trace and write these letters and numerals that have horizontal lines.
Start at the green dot.

e t f z A G F I 5

e t f z A G F I 5 ✔

Write the sentence.

Some strokes are horizontal lines.

Some strokes are horizontal lines

Circle Lines

Some letters and numerals have forward circle or backward circle lines.
Trace the circle or part of the circle in each letter and numeral.

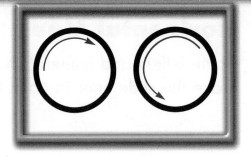

c   e   g   C   O   b   p   2   3

Trace and write these letters and numerals that have circle lines.
Start at the green dot.

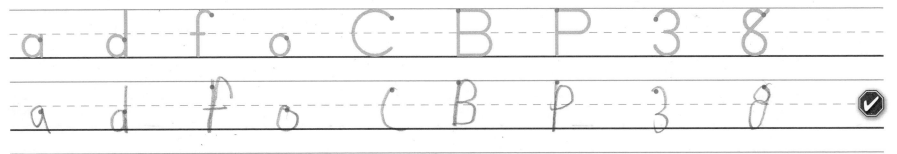

a   d   f   o   C   B   P   3   8

Write the sentence.

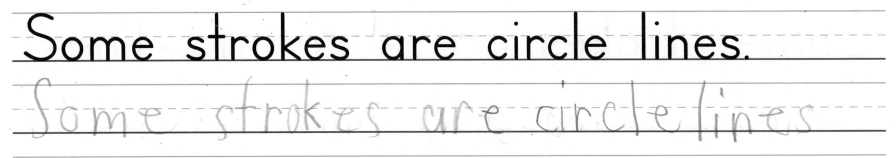

Some strokes are circle lines.

Slant Lines

Some letters and numerals have lines that slant left or slant right.
Trace the slant lines in each letter and numeral.

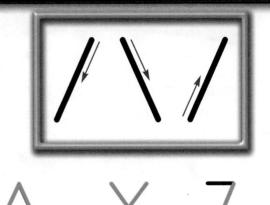

x   z   k   v   W   Q   A   X   7

Trace and write these letters and numerals that have slant lines.
Start at the green dot.

w   y   z   V   X   Q   Y   Z   K   7

w   y   z   V   X   Q   Y   Z   K   7

Write the sentence.

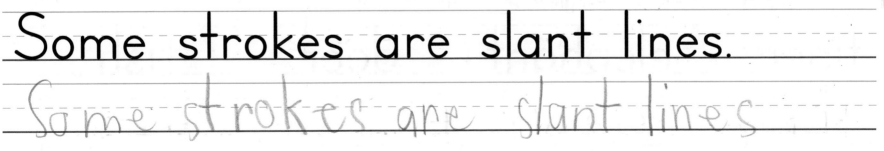

Some strokes are slant lines.

Some strokes are slant lines

Make your writing easy to read.
Look at the shape of your letters.

Handwriting Tutor

Manuscript writing has 4 kinds of lines.			
vertical	horizontal	circle	slant
|	—	c ɔ o	/\

Write the words. Pull down straight or push up straight to write vertical lines.

parrot   snail   newt   dog

parrot   snail   newt   dog

Write the words. Slide left or slide right to write horizontal lines.

tiger   elephant   deer   fish

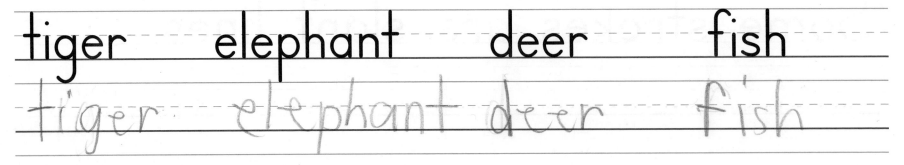

tiger   elephant   deer   fish

Write the words. Circle forward or circle backward to write circle lines.

cow   goat   pig   duck

cow   goat   pig   duck

Write the words. Slant left or slant right to write slant lines.

fox   lizard   wolf   skunk

My Own Writing   Write a sentence about your favorite animal.

15

Handwriting Tutor

Make your writing easy to read.
Look at the size of your letters.

Tall Letters

Tall letters touch the headline.

A b C

Short Letters

Short letters touch the midline.

a   e   o

Short Letters With Descenders

Some letters go below the baseline.

y   j   g

Write the words. Make sure your tall letters touch the headline.

hamster   rabbit   frog   cat

salamander   goldfish   turtle

Write the words. Make sure your short letters touch the midline.

lion   bear   mouse   zebra

Write the words. Make sure your letters with descenders go below
the baseline and touch the next line.

jaguar   quail   penguin

My Own Writing Write a sentence about a pet you know.

Size

Circle a word you wrote that has good size.

17

Handwriting Tutor

Make your writing easy to read.
Look at the spacing between letters and words.

PEACH STREET

These letters are too close.

Peach Street

These letters are too far apart.

Peach Street

Write the street names. Make sure your spacing between letters is just right.

Cherry Lane   Apple Road

There should be space for your little finger or a paper clip between words. Write the sentence.

Who lives on Banana Avenue?

Find the spacing mistakes in each sentence. Write the sentences correctly.

Sally is going to ride.

Kam plays o n GrapeRoad.

Tara lives on P e a r Drive.

My Own Writing Make up a street name. Write about what happens on that street.
Use good spacing between your letters and words.

Spacing

Circle a word you wrote that has good spacing.

19

Handwriting Tutor

Make your writing easy to read.
Look at the slant of your letters.

Here's a good way to check the slant of your letters.
Draw lines through each vertical stroke.

blueberries

If the lines you drew are straight up and down,
your word has good slant.

Write the words. Draw lines to check your slant.

bananas   strawberries

Write the sentence. Draw lines to check your slant.

I made an apple pie by myself.

These things will help you write with good vertical slant.
1. Position your paper properly.
2. Pull your strokes down in the correct direction.
3. Shift your paper as you write.

Write the words correctly. Make sure your writing has good slant.

Left-Handed Writers **Right-Handed Writers**

orange   peach   pear   kiwi

plum   apricot   grapes

My Own Writing   Write a sentence about a fruit you like.

Slant

Circle a word you wrote that has good slant.

21

Writing Numerals

1   2   3   4   5

Trace and write.

1   1   4   4   4   4   4   4 ✔

2   2   2   2   2   2 ✔   5   5   5   5   5   5 ✔

3   3   3   3   3   3 ✔

My Own Writing   Write a number sentence. Use a plus sign (+).

6 7 8 9 10

Trace and write.

6 6 6 6 6 6   9 9 9 9 9 9

7 7 7 7 7 7   10 10 10 10 10

8 8 8 8 8 8

My Own Writing   Write a number sentence. Use a minus sign (–).

Write the license number of the blue car.

Write the license number of the red truck.

Write the number of the street.

Write the number that tells how fast to drive.

Write the numbers on the doors.

My Own Writing Write about something that you see in the picture.

Trace and write.

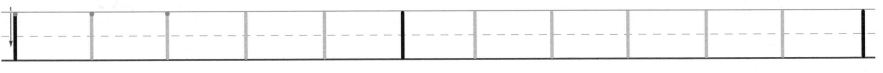

Handwriting Tutor

Stroke descriptions to guide letter formation at home:

1. Pull down straight.

1. Pull down straight. Lift.
2. Dot.

1. Pull down straight. Lift.
2. Slide right.

Stop and Check

Circle your best l.
Circle your best i.
Circle your best t.

Write the words about books.

title   author   illustrator

fiction   nonfiction   page

sentence   mystery   picture

My Own Writing Write a sentence about the kind of books you like.

Shape

Circle your best letter that has a vertical line.

Trace and write.

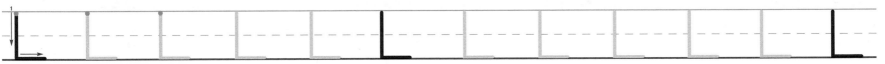

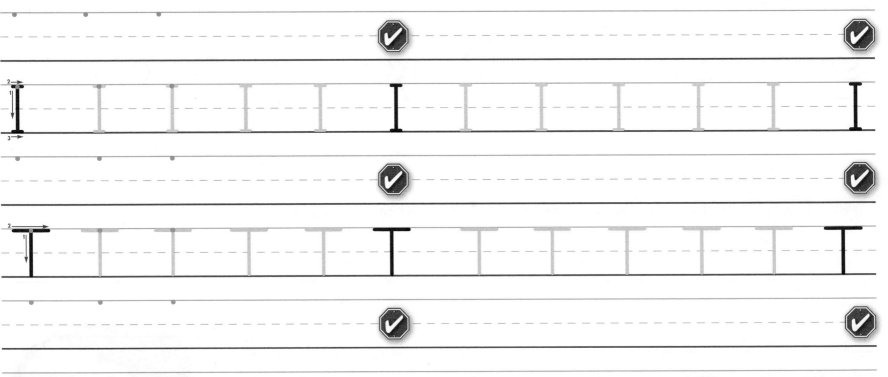

Handwriting Tutor

Stroke descriptions to guide letter formation at home:

1. Pull down straight. Slide right.

1. Pull down straight. Lift.
2. Slide right. Lift.
3. Slide right.

1. Pull down straight. Lift.
2. Slide right.

Stop and Check

Circle your best L.

Circle your best I.

Circle your best T.

Write the sentences about books.

Let's visit the library.

Is there a book for me?

The man at the desk will help you.

My Own Writing Write a sentence about a book you have read.

Size

Circle a word you wrote that has good size.

Trace and write.

o o o o o o o o o o o o

✓ ✓

a a a a a a a a a a a a

✓ ✓

d d d d d d d d d d d d

✓ ✓

Handwriting Tutor

Stroke descriptions to guide letter formation at home:

o
I. Circle back all the way around.

a
I. Circle back all the way around; push up straight. Pull down straight.

d
I. Circle back all the way around; push up straight. Pull down straight.

Stop and Check

Circle your best **o**.
Circle your best **a**.
Circle your best **d**.

Write the words that name landforms.

desert bay island

ocean mountain valley

plain dune canyon

My Own Writing Write a sentence about a landform you have seen.

Spacing

Circle two words with good spacing between them.

Trace and write.

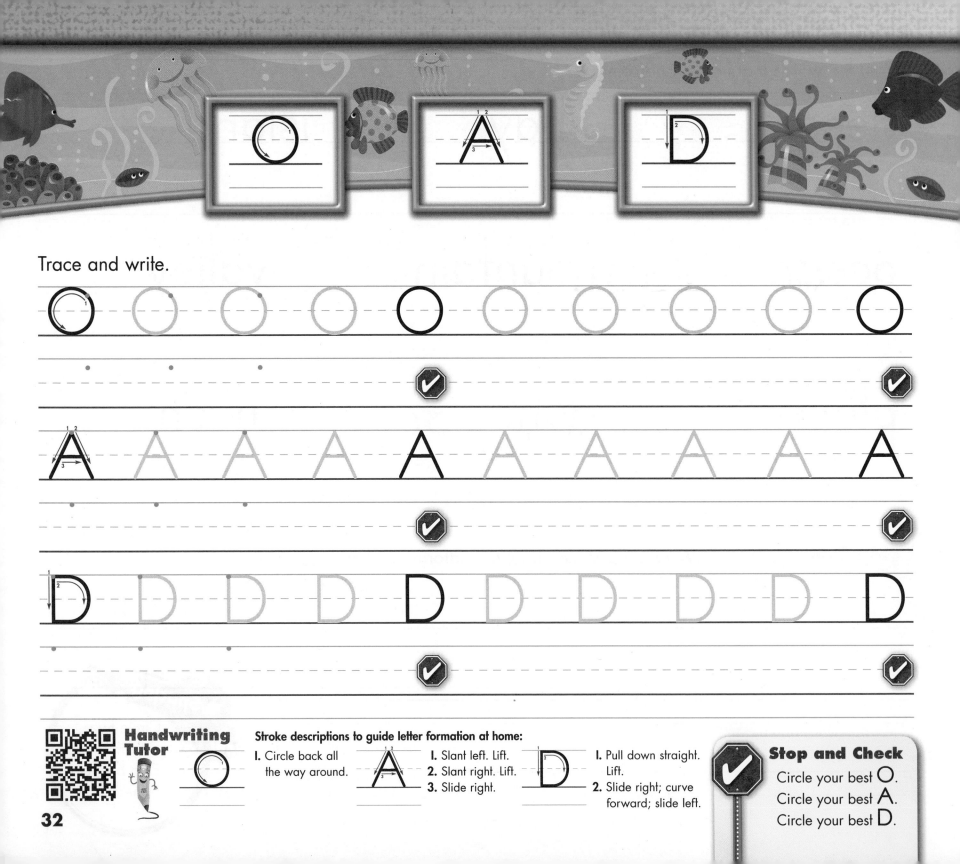

O O O O O O O O O O

A A A A A A A A A A

D D D D D D D D D D

Handwriting Tutor

Stroke descriptions to guide letter formation at home:

O
1. Circle back all the way around.

A
1. Slant left. Lift.
2. Slant right. Lift.
3. Slide right.

D
1. Pull down straight. Lift.
2. Slide right; curve forward; slide left.

Stop and Check

Circle your best O.
Circle your best A.
Circle your best D.

Write the sentences about landforms.

Oceans cover part of Earth.

A continent is huge.

Deserts are dry places.

My Own Writing Write a sentence about the continent you live on.

Slant

Circle a letter that is straight up and down.

Ll Ii Tt Oo Aa Dd

Write the list of holidays.

Our Favorite Holidays

Independence Day

Thanksgiving Day

Arbor Day   Labor Day

34

Write the invitation to a holiday party. Leave space for margins.

It's a Party!

Date: Labor Day
Time: 11:00 A.M.
Place: Olivia's House
Let's all have fun!

Write the story.
Make your writing easy to read. Be sure to leave space for margins.

The race began. As Ian ran, he

felt something odd. His shoe came

untied! He knew he must never

give up. So one foot was bare

when Ian crossed the finish line.

When Ian crossed the finish line

Is your writing easy to read?

Shape Circle your best letter that has a ○ line.

Size Circle your best short letter.

Spacing Circle two words that have space for between them.

Slant Circle a letter that is straight up and down.

Trace and write.

c c c c c c c c c c c c c c

e e e e e e e e e e e e e

f f f f f f f f f f f f f

Handwriting Tutor

Stroke descriptions to guide letter formation at home:

c
1. Circle back.

e
1. Slide right.
   Circle back.

f
1. Curve back; pull down straight. Lift.
2. Slide right.

Stop and Check

Circle your best c.
Circle your best e.
Circle your best f.

Write the words that name breakfast foods.

cereal
cereal

eggs
eggs

fruit
fruit

cheese
cheese

bagels
bagels

waffles
waffles

corn muffins
corn muffins

juice
juice

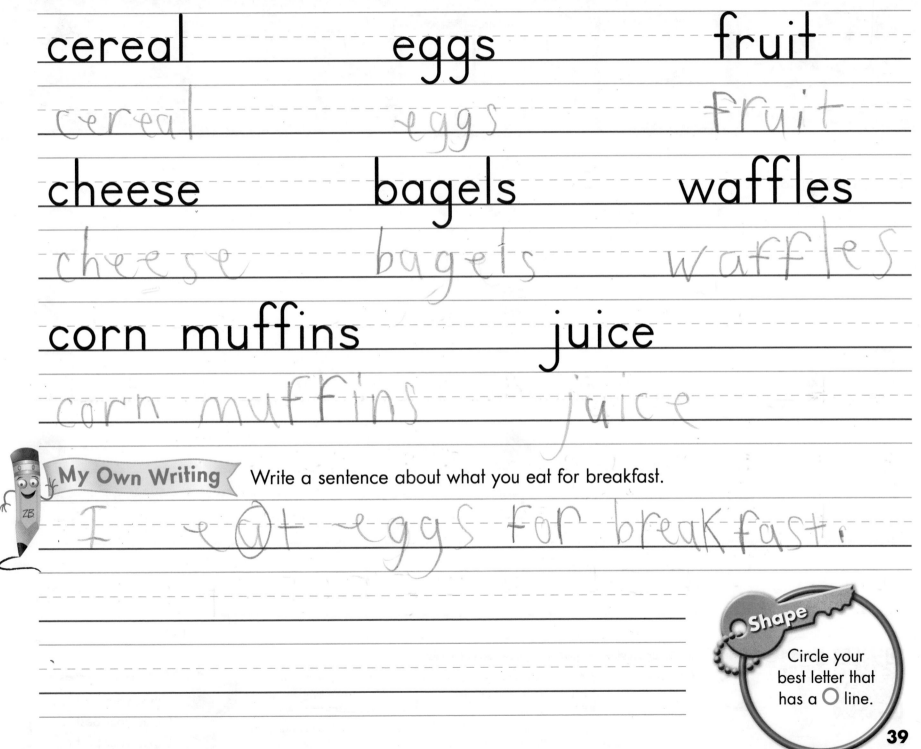

My Own Writing Write a sentence about what you eat for breakfast.

I eat eggs for breakfast.

Shape
Circle your best letter that has a ◯ line.

39

Trace and write.

Handwriting Tutor

Stroke descriptions to guide letter formation at home:

C
1. Circle back.

E
1. Pull down straight. Lift.
2. Slide right. Lift.
3. Slide right; stop short. Lift.
4. Slide right.

F
1. Pull down straight. Lift.
2. Slide right. Lift.
3. Slide right; stop short.

Stop and Check

Circle your best C.

Circle your best E.

Circle your best F.

Write the sentences about eating breakfast.

Everyone should eat breakfast.

Everyone should eat breakfast.

Food gives your body energy.

Food gives your body energy

Choose good foods to eat.

Choose good foods to eat.

Write a sentence about your favorite snack.

My favorite snak is a
Bacon sandwitch.

Size

Circle your
best tall letter.

Trace and write.

g g g g g g **g** g g g g g **g**

j j j j j **j** j j j j j **j**

q q q q q **q** q q q q q **q**

Handwriting Tutor

g

Stroke descriptions to guide letter formation at home:

1. Circle back all the way around; push up straight. Pull down straight; curve back.

j

1. Pull down straight; curve back. Lift.
2. Dot.

q

1. Circle back all the way around; push up straight. Pull down straight; curve forward.

Stop and Check

Circle your best g.
Circle your best j.
Circle your best q.

Write the words about telling jokes.

jokes   question   enjoy

giggle   squeal   laugh

funny   quick   jolly

My Own Writing Where can a 3,000-pound elephant sit? Write a sentence to answer the question.

Spacing

Circle two letters with good spacing between them.

Answer: It can sit anywhere it wants.

43

Trace and write.

G G G G G G G G G G G

J J J J J J J J J J J

Q Q Q Q Q Q Q Q Q Q Q

Handwriting Tutor

Stroke descriptions to guide letter formation at home:

G — 1. Circle back. Slide left.

J — 1. Pull down straight; curve back. Lift. 2. Slide right.

Q — 1. Circle back all the way around. Lift. 2. Slant right.

Stop and Check

Circle your best G.
Circle your best J.
Circle your best Q.

Write the sentences about jokes.

Jokes are such fun to tell.

Gil's joke made me giggle.

Quentin laughed at the joke, too.

My Own Writing Write a sentence about what makes you laugh.

Cc Ee Ff Gg Jj Qq

Write the names of places.

Mojave Desert   Quebec

Eugene, Oregon   Georgia

Grand Canyon   Jamestown

Ellis Island   Petrified Forest

The Grand Canyon

Every year, quite a few visitors come. Just look at the view! Fabulous colors glow like jewels here.

Write the paragraph about the Grand Canyon. Indent the first line of the paragraph. Be sure to leave space for margins.

Stop and Check

Circle a word you wrote that has good size.

Slant

Spacing

Size

Shape

Write the directions to a friend's house.
Make your writing easy to read, leaving space for margins.

Follow Dodd Lane through town.

Turn left at a round green bush.

Before the end of the road,

try to get in the right lane.

At the fork in the road, go right.

Is your writing easy to read?

Shape
Circle your best letter that has a ○ line.

Size
Circle your best short letter.

Spacing
Circle two words that have space for between them.

Slant
Circle a letter that is straight up and down.

Trace and write.

U u U U U U u U U U u U U U u

S s S S S S s S S S S s S S S s

Handwriting Tutor

u

Stroke descriptions to guide letter formation at home:

I. Pull down straight; curve forward; push up. Pull down straight.

u

I. Curve back; curve forward.

s

Stop and Check

Circle your best u.
Circle your best s.

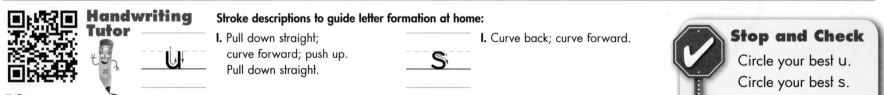

Write the words about sea life.

seaweed   fish   sea horse

tiger shark   underwater

turtle   swim   octopus

My Own Writing   Write a sentence about something that lives in the ocean.

51

U   S

Trace and write.

U U U U U U U U U U U U U

S S S S S S S S S S S S S

Handwriting Tutor

U

Stroke descriptions to guide letter formation at home:

U
1. Pull down straight; curve forward; push up.

S
1. Curve back; curve forward.

Stop and Check

Circle your best U.
Circle your best S.

Write the facts about seals.

Seals can swim very fast.

Usually, seals eat fish.

Seals make a sound like a horn.

My Own Writing Write a sentence about a sea animal you like.

Size

Circle your best short letter.

Trace and write.

b b b b b **b** b b b b b **b**

p p p p p **p** p p p p p **p**

r r r r r **r** r r r r r **r**

Handwriting Tutor

Stroke descriptions to guide letter formation at home:

b
l. Pull down straight. Push up; circle forward.

p
l. Pull down straight. Push up; circle forward.

r
l. Pull down straight. Push up; curve forward.

Stop and Check

Circle your best **b**.

Circle your best **p**.

Circle your best **r**.

Write the words that name things found near a pond.

bugs   chipmunk   bridge

rabbit   frogs   tadpoles

beaver   reeds   raccoon

My Own Writing   Write a sentence about an animal that lives near a pond.

Spacing

Circle two words with good spacing between them.

B   P   R

Trace and write.

B B B B B B B B B B B B

P P P P P P P P P P P P

R R R R R R R R R R R R

Handwriting Tutor

Stroke descriptions to guide letter formation at home:

B
1. Pull down straight. Lift.
2. Slide right; curve forward; slide left. Slide right; curve forward; slide left.

P
1. Pull down straight. Lift.
2. Slide right; curve forward; slide left.

R
1. Pull down straight. Lift.
2. Slide right; curve forward; slide left. Slant right.

Stop and Check

Circle your best B.

Circle your best P.

Circle your best R.

Write the sentences about pond life.

Reeds grow near the pond.

Busy beavers build dams.

Ponds are full of life!

My Own Writing   Write a sentence about something that might happen by a pond.

Slant

Circle a word that is straight up and down.

57

Trace and write.

Stroke descriptions to guide letter formation at home:

l. Pull down straight. Push up; curve forward; pull down straight.

l. Pull down straight. Push up; curve forward; pull down straight. Push up; curve forward; pull down straight.

l. Pull down straight. Push up; curve forward; pull down straight.

Stop and Check

Circle your best **n**.

Circle your best **m**.

Circle your best **h**.

Write the words about math.

count   half   money

measure   tens   many

even   number   hundreds

My Own Writing   Write a sentence about a way that you use numbers.

Shape

Circle your best letter that has a / line.

59

Trace and write.

N N N N N N N N N N N N

M M M M M M M M M M M M

H H H H H H H H H H H H

Handwriting Tutor

Stroke descriptions to guide letter formation at home:

1. Pull down straight. Lift.
2. Slant right. Push up straight.

1. Pull down straight. Lift.
2. Slant right. Slant up. Pull down straight.

1. Pull down straight. Lift.
2. Pull down straight. Lift.
3. Slide right.

Stop and Check

Circle your best N.

Circle your best M.

Circle your best H.

Write the sentences about the number nine.

My favorite numeral is nine.

Nine plus one. What is the sum?

How many threes equal nine?

My Own Writing What is your favorite number? Write a sentence that tells why it is your favorite.

Size

Circle a word you wrote that has good size.

Uu Ss Bb Pp Rr Nn Mm Hh

Write the book titles. Remember to underline.

<u>Madeline's Rescue</u>

<u>Babar Saves the Day</u>

<u>Teach Us, Amelia Bedelia</u>

<u>The Napping House</u>

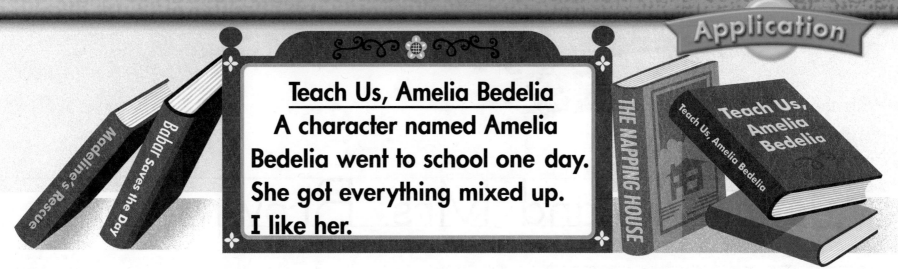

Teach Us, Amelia Bedelia

A character named Amelia Bedelia went to school one day. She got everything mixed up. I like her.

Write the sentences about the funny book. Remember to indent the first line and leave space for margins.

Stop and Check

Circle a word you wrote that has good spacing.

Slant

Spacing

Size

Shape

Write the business letter.
Leave space for margins.
Make your writing easy to read.

Dear Mr. and Mrs. Brown,

Do you need help on your farm?

I think I am a good farmhand.

Yours truly,

Marcus Spencer

Is your writing easy to read?

Shape
Circle your best letter that has a | line.

Size
Circle your best tall letter.

Spacing
Circle two words that have space for between them.

Slant
Circle a letter that is straight up and down.

Trace and write.

v v v v v v v v v v v v

y y y y y y y y y y y y

w w w w w w w w w w w w

Handwriting Tutor

Stroke descriptions to guide letter formation at home:

v
1. Slant right.
   Slant up.

y
1. Slant right.
   Lift.
2. Slant left.

w
1. Slant right.
   Slant up.
   Slant right.
   Slant up.

Stop and Check

Circle your best v.

Circle your best y.

Circle your best w.

Write the words about weather.

vapor   warm   above

snowy   cloudy   rainy

windy   sunny   twister

My Own Writing Write a sentence about today's weather.

Spacing

Circle two letters with good spacing between them.

Trace and write.

V V V V V V V V V

Y Y Y Y Y Y Y Y Y

W W W W W W W W W

Handwriting Tutor

Stroke descriptions to guide letter formation at home:

V 1. Slant right.
   Slant up.

Y 1. Slant right. Lift.
   2. Slant left. Pull down straight.

W 1. Slant right.
   Slant up.
   Slant right.
   Slant up.

Stop and Check
Circle your best V.
Circle your best Y.
Circle your best W.

Write the sentences about a windy day.

Windy days can be nice.

Oh boy! Your kite can fly high!

Val's kite can soar like a plane.

My Own Writing Write a sentence about your favorite kind of weather.

Slant

Circle a letter you wrote that is straight up and down.

Trace and write.

X X X X X X X X X X X X X

k k k k k k k k k k k k k

z z z z z z z z z z z z z

Handwriting Tutor

Stroke descriptions to guide letter formation at home:

X
1. Slant right. Lift.
2. Slant left.

k
1. Pull down straight. Lift.
2. Slant left. Slant right.

z
1. Slide right. Slant left. Slide right.

Stop and Check

Circle your best x.

Circle your best k.

Circle your best z.

Write the words about building.

cement mixer   bricks

dump truck   work zone

bulldozer   backhoe

My Own Writing Write a sentence about something you would like to build.

Trace and write.

X X X X X X X X X X

K K K K K K K K K K

Z Z Z Z Z Z Z Z Z Z

Handwriting Tutor

Stroke descriptions to guide letter formation at home:

X
1. Slant right. Lift.
2. Slant left.

K
1. Pull down straight. Lift.
2. Slant left. Slant right.

Z
1. Slide right. Slant left. Slide right.

Stop and Check
Circle your best X.
Circle your best K.
Circle your best Z.

Write the words found on the signs.

Building Zone   Keep Out

EXIT   CAUTION

Slow   WALK

My Own Writing Write words from other signs you have seen.

ZB

Size

Circle your best tall letter.

Vv Yy Ww Xx Kk Zz

Write the state names and abbreviations.

NV Nevada   WY Wyoming

TX Texas   AR Arkansas

AZ Arizona   WI Wisconsin

Today is Wednesday. We drove all day. I saw TX or NV on many license plates. I know TX stands for Texas. NV must mean Nevada.

Write the travel journal. Remember to indent the first line of the paragraph and leave space for margins.

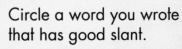

Stop and Check

Circle a word you wrote that has good slant.

75

Slant

Spacing

Size

Shape

Write the personal narrative.
Make your writing easy to read. Be sure to leave space for margins.

I went to town with my mother.

We rode on the subway.

It was very crowded.

Two men gave us their seats.

"How kind," my mother said.

Is your writing easy to read?

Shape
Circle your best letter that has a l line.

Size
Circle your best short letter.

Spacing
Circle two words that have space for between them.

Slant
Circle a word you wrote that is straight up and down.

Write the name for each letter of the alphabet.

Azize   Bobby   Connor

Dionne   Elijah   Felipe

Greg   Howard   Isabel

Jordan   Kim   Lily   Max

Noah   Olivia   Pasqual

Quintana   Rick   Sofia

Terry   Ursula   Victor

Wan   Xavier   Yolanda

Zuria

My writing has good Shape ☐
My writing has good Size ☐
My writing has good Spacing ☐
My writing has good Slant ☐

79

Number Fun

Fill in the missing dates on the calendar.

MARCH

Sunday	Monday	Tuesday	Wednesday	Thursday	Friday	Saturday
	1	2	_____	_____	_____	_____
_____	8	_____	10	11	12 soccer game	13
14	15	_____	17	18	19 No School	20
21	_____	23 Emily's birthday	_____	25 picnic at White Rock Lake	_____	27
_____	30	31 class play				

Look at the calendar. Then write sentences to answer the questions.

1. On what date is the class play?

_____

_____

2. On what date is the picnic at White Rock Lake?

_____

_____

3. What will happen on March 12?

_____

_____

4. On what date is Emily's birthday?

_____

_____

Spacing

Circle a word you wrote that has good spacing.

Visit Number Land

Write the addresses for five of the houses you see.

_____

_____

_____

_____

_____

_____

_____

_____

Choose one house from the picture. Write the address of the house. Tell about who might live there. Leave space for margins.

STONE ST
LAKE AVE

Slant

Circle a numeral you wrote that is straight up and down.

83

Why Do You Write?

On the following pages, you will write about many interesting things. You will write for many reasons. Thinking about Shape, Size, Spacing, and Slant will help you make your writing easy to read. Read to find out why these students are writing.

My Own Writing   Write a sentence about something you have written.

Let's Get Ready to Write

Before you write, think about your topic.
Make a list of ideas for your story.

Here are some ideas for a story about a fox.
Write words that tell what the fox is like and what it does.

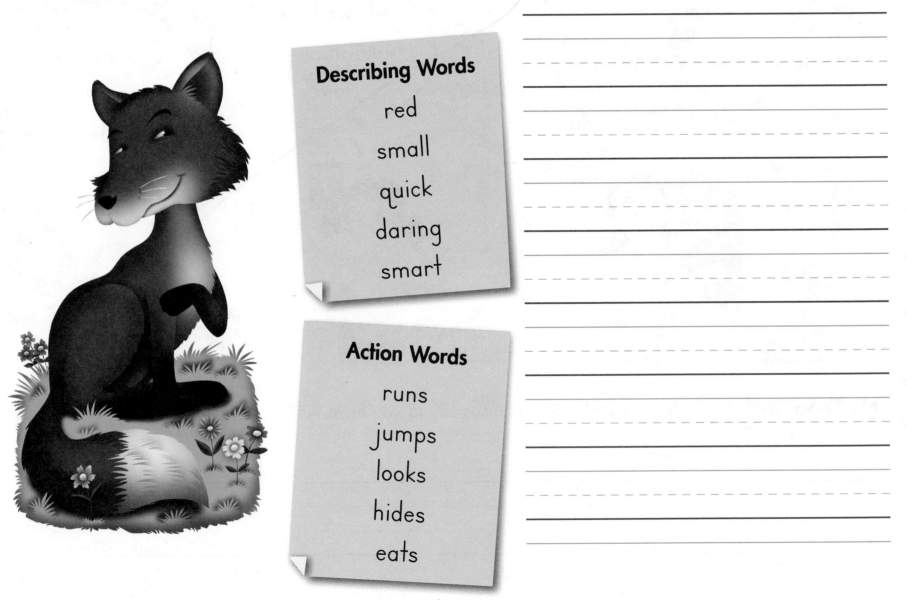

Describing Words

red

small

quick

daring

smart

Action Words

runs

jumps

looks

hides

eats

Choose an animal to write about. Draw a picture in the box.
Then write words that tell what the animal is like and what it does.

Making a Web

Write the words to complete the Web.

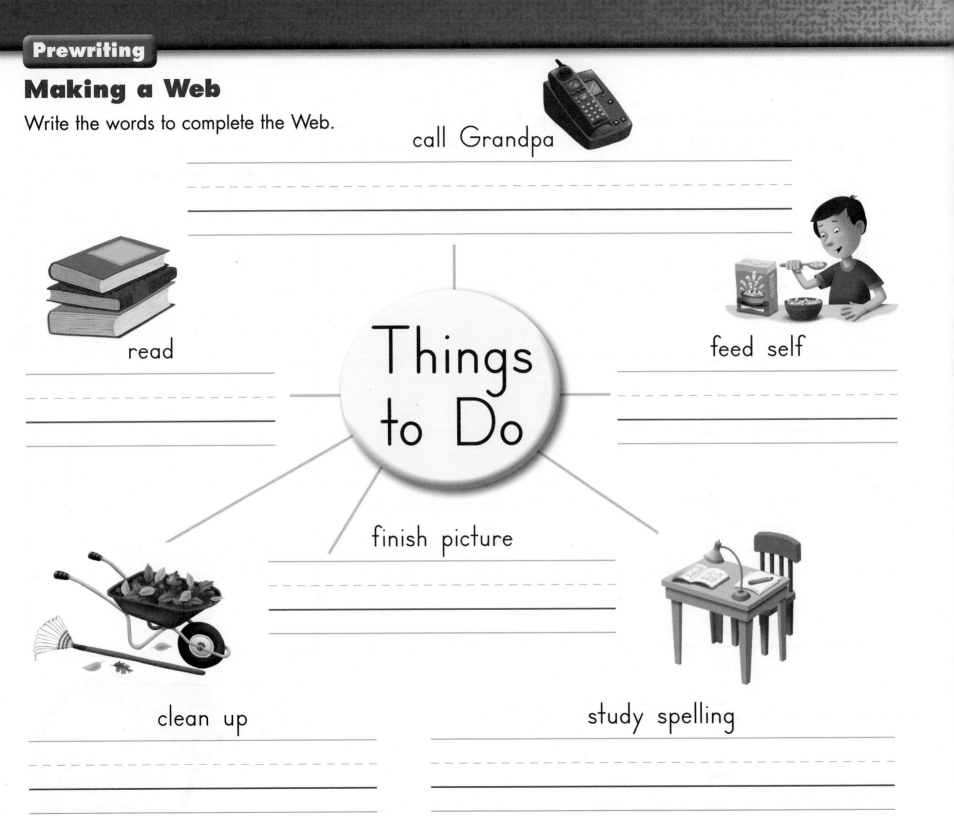

call Grandpa

read

feed self

Things to Do

finish picture

clean up

study spelling

Complete this Web by writing things you need to do.

My Things
to Do

Size

Circle three words you wrote that have good size.

It's So Cold!

| mittens | hat | scarf | gloves |
| sledding | skiing | skating | snowman |

Write the names of things to wear or do when it is cold outside.

Write a story about a snowy day. Remember to indent the first line of the paragraph and leave space for margins.

Spacing

Circle a word you wrote that has good spacing.

It's So Warm!

hat umbrella sunglasses
swimsuit T-shirt
radio
cooler towel
blanket
sunblock sandals

Write the things you see on a warm day at the beach.

Write a story about what you like to do when the weather is warm.
Be sure to leave space for margins.

Slant

Circle three words you wrote that have good slant.

E-mail

screen   e-mail

mouse   keyboard

online   mousepad

click   print

World Wide Web

Write the words about computers.

Write an e-mail to a friend. Be sure to leave space for margins.

Shape

Circle three words you wrote that have good shape.

My Favorite Meal

Sweet	**Sour**	**Salty**	**Spicy**
strawberries	lemons	pretzels	salsa
watermelons	pickles	peanuts	mustard
cherries	grapefruits	chips	chili
bananas	limes	crackers	peppers

Choose two of the lists.
Write one list here.

Write another list here.

_____

_____

Write about your favorite meal. Describe how the food looks and tastes.
Be sure to leave space for margins.

Size

Circle a word you wrote that has good size.

Helping Hands

share your supplies

put books away

help teacher

take turns

clean up

pass out papers

Write things you can do to help at school.
Use the words above or add other ideas.

Write a list of ways to help at home. Be sure to leave space for margins.

Ways to Help at Home:

I Can Do It!

Here are some easy steps to follow to make a healthy sandwich.

You will need:

two slices of bread

cheese

sliced tomatoes

lettuce leaves

1. Put cheese on a slice of bread.
2. Cover cheese with tomato.
3. Also cover with lettuce.
4. Cover with other slice of bread.
5. Enjoy!

Write the steps to follow when making a cheese, lettuce, and tomato sandwich.

Think of a food you can make. Write the steps to follow when making it. Leave space for margins.

Slant

Circle a word you wrote that has good slant.

In a Night Sky

Write the names of things you see in a night sky.

Look at the picture of the moon.
Write sentences to tell what you know about the moon.

Shape

Circle three words you wrote that have good shape.

My Favorite Color

Write the color words. Then circle the color you like best.

red

orange

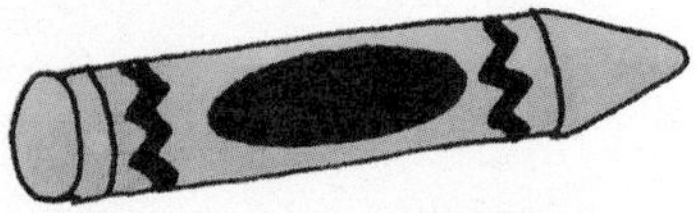

yellow

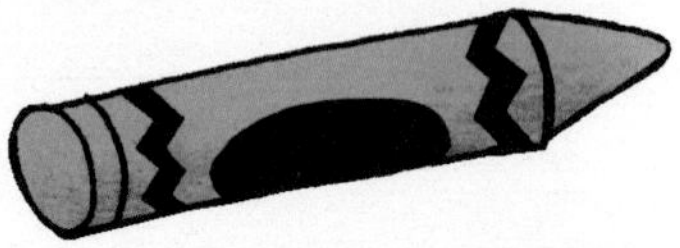

green

blue

purple

black

white

Write your favorite color. Then give reasons that color is best. Include a concluding sentence. Remember to leave space for margins.

My favorite color is

Book Review

Draw a character or an event from a book you have read. Then write the title of the book.

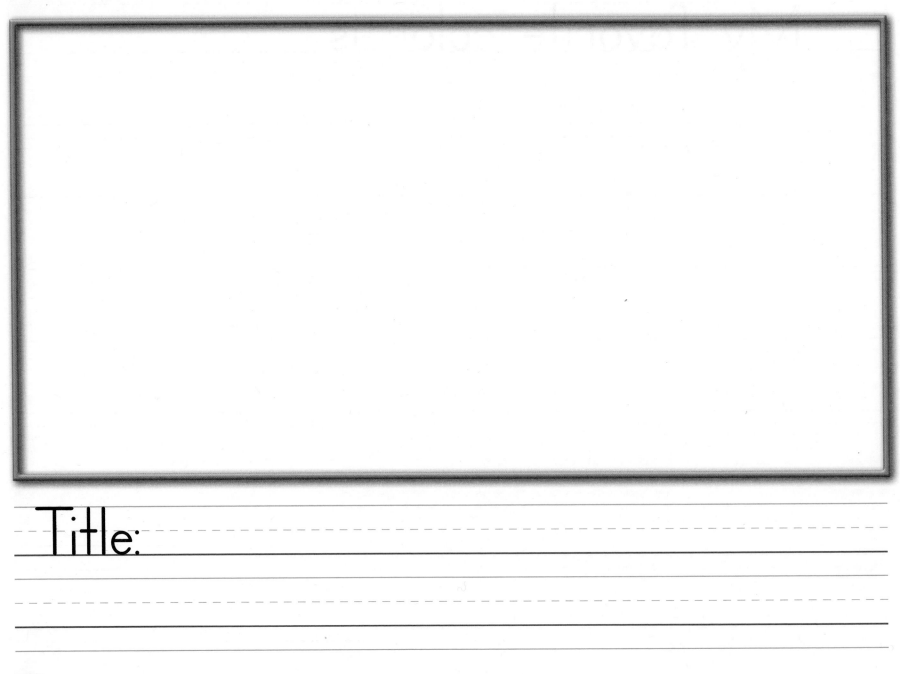

Title:

Write your opinion about the book. Include at least two reasons to support your opinion. Finish your writing with a concluding statement explaining why your classmates should or should not read the book. Remember to indent the first line of each paragraph you write and leave space for margins.

The Best Pet

Write a list of pets. Then draw a picture of the pet you like best.

Write your opinion about the best pet. Include at least two reasons to support your opinion. Include a concluding sentence. Remember to leave space for margins.

The best pet is

My Classroom

Write facts about your classroom. You might include what your classroom looks like, how many students are in your class, or what you learn in your classroom. Remember to indent the first line of each paragraph you write and leave space for margins.

Handwriting and the Writing Process

Write about a special place you visited. Tell what you saw there.
Write on a piece of writing paper. Follow these five steps as you write.

1. Prewriting

Plan ideas for your writing.
Use good handwriting
so you can read your ideas later.

2. Drafting

Write your ideas in sentences.
Your writing should be easy to read.

3. Revising

Revise your writing.
Make changes so that it says what you mean.

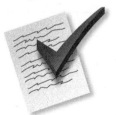

4. Editing

Check your spelling, punctuation, and handwriting.
Make sure your writing is easy to read.

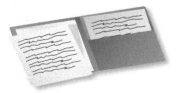

5. Publishing

Share your writing with others.
Use your best handwriting.

Writing Quickly

Make your writing easy to read.
Write this saying. Leave space for margins.

Mighty oaks from
little acorns grow.

Now write it again. Try to write faster this time.

Write the saying again. Try to write even faster.
Make sure your writing is easy to read.

Now read your writing. Ask others to read it, too.
Then circle Yes or No next to each sentence.

My writing is easy for me to read.   Yes   No

My writing is easy for others to read.   Yes   No

Writing Easily

When your writing flows easily, you don't have to worry about your handwriting. You can just think about what you want to say.

Read the writing prompt below. Write your story on the lines. Let your handwriting flow easily.

> Write a story about what you see in the picture. Tell what might happen next.

Now read your final writing. Circle Yes or No to respond to each statement.
Then show your writing to another reader, either a classmate or your teacher.
Ask that person to circle Yes or No beside each statement.

	My Evaluation	My Classmate's or Teacher's Evaluation
The writing is easy to read.	Yes No	Yes No
The writing has good Shape.	Yes No	Yes No
The writing has good Size.	Yes No	Yes No
The writing has good Spacing.	Yes No	Yes No
The writing has good Slant.	Yes No	Yes No

Show What You Can Do

City
In the morning the city
Spreads its wings
Making a song
In stone that sings.

Write the title and the first four lines of the poem in your best handwriting.
Be sure to leave space for margins.

In the evening the city
Goes to bed
Hanging lights
About its head.

by Langston Hughes

Write the next four lines here. Leave space for margins.

117

Write the Sentence

The quick brown fox jumps over the lazy dog.

Record of Student's Handwriting Skills

Manuscript

	Needs Improvement	Shows Mastery		Needs Improvement	Shows Mastery
Uses good sitting position	☐	☐	Writes **u, s**	☐	☐
Positions paper correctly	☐	☐	Writes **U, S**	☐	☐
Holds pencil correctly	☐	☐	Writes **b, p, r**	☐	☐
Writes vertical lines	☐	☐	Writes **B, P, R**	☐	☐
Writes horizontal lines	☐	☐	Writes **n, m, h**	☐	☐
Writes circle lines	☐	☐	Writes **N, M, H**	☐	☐
Writes slant lines	☐	☐	Writes **v, y, w**	☐	☐
Writes numerals **1–10**	☐	☐	Writes **V, Y, W**	☐	☐
Writes **l, i, t**	☐	☐	Writes **x, k, z**	☐	☐
Writes **L, I, T**	☐	☐	Writes **X, K, Z**	☐	☐
Writes **o, a, d**	☐	☐	Writes with correct shape	☐	☐
Writes **O, A, D**	☐	☐	Writes with correct size	☐	☐
Writes **c, e, f**	☐	☐	Writes with correct spacing	☐	☐
Writes **C, E, F**	☐	☐	Writes with correct slant	☐	☐
Writes **g, j, q**	☐	☐	Regularly checks written work for legibility	☐	☐
Writes **G, J, Q**	☐	☐			

Index

Automaticity, See Writing Easily; Writing Quickly

Basic strokes
- circle lines, 12, 14–15
- horizontal lines, 11, 14
- slant lines, 13, 14–15
- vertical lines, 10, 14

Evaluation, 5
- posttest, 116–117
- pretest, 6–7
- Record of Student's Handwriting Skills, 119
- self-evaluation, 10, 11, 12, 13, 15, 17, 19, 21, 22, 23, 26, 27, 28, 29, 30, 31, 32, 33, 37, 38, 39, 40, 41, 42, 43, 44, 45, 47, 49, 50, 51, 52, 53, 54, 55, 56, 57, 58, 59, 60, 61, 63, 65, 66, 67, 68, 69, 70, 71, 72, 73, 75, 77, 78, 79, 81, 83, 87, 89, 91, 93, 95, 97, 99, 101, 103, 113, 115, 117

Grammar, usage, and mechanics
- adjectives, 86, 97
- nouns, 14–15, 16–17, 21, 71, 90, 92, 94, 96, 102
- verbs, 86, 98, 100

Guidelines, using, 5

Indentation and margin practice, 6–7, 35, 36–37, 47, 48–49, 63, 64–65, 75, 76–77, 83, 91, 93, 95, 97, 99, 101, 103, 105, 107, 109, 110, 112–113, 114–115, 116–117

Keys to Legibility, 5
- shape, 14–15, 27, 36–37, 39, 48–49, 51, 59, 64–65, 71, 76–77, 79, 87, 95, 103, 115, 117
- size, 16–17, 29, 36–37, 41, 48–49, 53, 61, 64–65, 73, 76–77, 79, 89, 97, 115, 117
- slant, 20–21, 33, 36–37, 45, 48–49, 57, 64–65, 69, 76–77, 79, 83, 93, 101, 115, 117
- spacing, 18–19, 31, 36–37, 43, 48–49, 55, 64–65, 67, 76–77, 79, 81, 91, 99, 115, 117

Left-handed writers, 8, 21

Legibility, See Keys to Legibility

Letter groupings
- lL, iI, tT, 26–29
- oO, aA, dD, 30–33
- cC, eE, fF, 38–41
- gG, jJ, qQ, 42–45
- uU, sS, 50–53
- bB, pP, rR, 54–57
- nN, mM, hH, 58–61
- vV, yY, wW, 66–69
- xX, kK, zZ, 70–73

Letters
- lowercase: **a,** 30–31; **b,** 54–55; **c,** 38–39; **d,** 30–31; **e,** 38–39; **f,** 38–39; **g,** 42–43; **h,** 58–59; **i,** 26–27; **j,** 42–43; **k,** 70–71; **l,** 26–27; **m,** 58–59; **n,** 58–59; **o,** 30–31; **p,** 54–55; **q,** 42–43; **r,** 54–55; **s,** 50–51; **t,** 26–27; **u,** 50–51; **v,** 66–67; **w,** 66–67; **x,** 70–71; **y,** 66–67; **z,** 70–71
- uppercase: **A,** 32–33; **B,** 56–57; **C,** 40–41; **D,** 32–33; **E,** 40–41; **F,** 40–41; **G,** 44–45; **H,** 60–61; **I,** 28–29; **J,** 44–45; **K,** 72–73; **L,** 28–29; **M,** 60–61; **N,** 60–61; **O,** 32–33; **P,** 56–57; **Q,** 44–45; **R,** 56–57; **S,** 52–53; **T,** 28–29; **U,** 52–53; **V,** 68–69; **W,** 68–69; **X,** 72–73; **Y,** 68–69; **Z,** 72–73

Manuscript maintenance, 78–79

Number words, writing, 59, 61

Numerals, writing, 22–25, 80–81, 82–83

Posttest, 116–117

Pretest, 6–7

Record of Student's Handwriting Skills, 119

Review, 24–25, 34, 46, 62, 74

Right-handed writers, 9, 21

Technology, 5, 8, 9, 14, 16, 18, 20, 22, 23, 26, 28, 30, 32, 38, 40, 42, 44, 50, 52, 54, 56, 58, 60, 66, 68, 70, 72

Writing applications, 35, 47, 63, 75, 86–87, 88–89, 90–91, 92–93, 94–95, 96–97, 98–99, 100–101, 102–103, 104–105, 106–107, 108–109, 110, 111

Writing Easily, 114–115

Writing in the text types
- Informative/Explanatory, 96–97, 98–99, 100–101, 102–103, 110, 111
- Narrative, 90–91, 92–93, 114–115
- Opinion, 104–105, 106–107, 108–109

Writing positions
- paper, 8–9, 21
- pencil, 8–9
- sitting, 8–9

Writing process, 84–85, 86–87, 88–89, 111

Writing Quickly, 112–113